Vulga
Variani

By the same author

Poetry Introduction 7
Faber and Faber

Steel Horizon: North Sea Poems
Incline Press

Ordinary Others
Drizzle-Dazzle

JONATHAN WONHAM

Vulgar
Variants

With illustrations by
SUZANNE SMITH

Dri**zz**l**e - D**a**zz**l**e**

First published in 2021 by
Drizzle-Dazzle
105 Benslow Lane
Hitchin, Herts SG4 9RA
UK

Poems © Jonathan Wonham 2021
www.jonathanwonham.com

Illustrations © Suzanne Smith 2021
www.saatchiart.com/account/artworks/509731

ISBNs
Hardback 978-1-8382880-4-4
Paperback 978-1-8382880-3-7

Printed and bound by 4edge Limited, UK

Contents

Doctor T

Former research scientist at the nuclear defence agency
Doctor T was a happy active fellow always running
everywhere no time to waste was one of the favourite
sayings of Doctor T an expert on the dynamics of nuclear
fission Doctor T had one day woken from an apocalyptic
vision of the fruits of his own research and decided to
become a physics teacher now Doctor T no longer wore a
radiation suit instead he wore a brown tweed jacket and a
checked shirt he had a trim moustache and a trim waist he
was all over a very trim figure Doctor T always progressed
all over school with haste the children liked Doctor T
mainly for his mistakes for example the time when Doctor
T was demonstrating the mechanical advantage of pulleys
and lifted himself on a swing by standing on it Doctor T
pulled his legs out from under him and cracked his nut on
the linoleum Doctor T was a hard nut to crack he lay on
his back some minutes when Doctor T came round he told
the class to wake up and follow him one of the favourite
sayings of Doctor T was wake up and follow me to the
bunker Doctor T usually said this to his own kids in the wee
small hours one of the achievements of Doctor T was to
build his own small bunker three hours distant from home

somewhere on the west coast where the post-apocalyptic air would be fresher the kids of Doctor T nowadays hated to wake up and hear wake up and follow me it meant a three hour drive to the west coast in the old and very safe car of Doctor T followed by a weekend in the cold underground chamber where the wife of Doctor T made the best of it reading the kids books and cooking meals from long life rations Doctor T only wished for them all a long life listening attentively to news on the long wave radio to see if the imminent threat had passed Doctor T had passed his whole life listening to various ultimatums dropped from on high now Doctor T had his own ultimate defence against whatever might come out of the sky and being a physicist and somewhat of an expert on plutonium Doctor T had worked out the required thickness of concrete above his head the required speed to cross the country in his very safe car Doctor T found the whole situation kept his mind very much alive although a little distracted and hence the mistakes made by Doctor T that kept the children so well amused like when he uncorked the mercury in his trouser pocket it was just an accident said Doctor T it wasn't like he had just blown up the nuclear test facility.

Moira Mackenzie

Moira Mackenzie put herself inside a plum for just a
little while it seemed a haven it was cool and sweet Moira
Mackenzie thought perhaps she'd died and gone to heaven
she stuck out her tongue and licked her lips there was only
a smooth membrane not elastified like her own skin none
of the faint bristles she remembered Moira Mackenzie
remembered finally to open her eyes and look out at the
room she had deserted it looked different so empty infertile
where could she grow in that room she rolled along the
table top propelling herself with her thoughts alone Moira
Mackenzie alone with her thoughts in a plum was now
looking at her children who were playing on the floor and
thinking about their teeth it made her almost faint to think
of their horrid gnashers Moira Mackenzie remembered
supervising the cleaning of them wished she had not how
hellish it was to think of those small unsupervised white
tusks it irked her how they played there knowing nothing
of her fear rolling stealthily across the table looking for a
place to quietly reside all her life Moira Mackenzie had
resided quietly in the sweetness of the world now Moira
Mackenzie had all the world's sweetness in her mouth it
made her mouth water so she wished all mouths were fruit
not machines of destruction she did not know she had

rolled so close to the table edge no one warned Moira Mackenzie how could they who thinks to warn a plum before it falls Moira Mackenzie felt frightened she watched her children's gawping mouths no noise came out only glistening white tusks she rolled backwards over the edge and into the fire grate splitting her plumpness a little on the hard tiles the juice leaked from the hole in her side she lay there still she was okay she had survived but survived for what Moira Mackenzie felt herself beginning to glow it was not her it was the electric bars Moira Mackenzie had previously turned up the heat it was feeling a little cold she was sensitive to the cold now she was sensitive to the heat her smooth skin quickly wrinkled it was the last thing Moira Mackenzie wished for her own doing her smooth skin wrinkling Moira Mackenzie felt oversweet jammy she tried to roll but could not her children heard her wheezing hiss and came to look but saw only a plum that had somehow fallen one said look and picked her up he sucked his fingers yuk he said for Moira Mackenzie was wet and broken she was sticky in his fingers one opened a window the other one threw her out Moira Mackenzie landed in the soil oh it felt good her juice soaked away leaves pitied her and quickly fell they turned to dust like tiny shrouds they buried her stony face in the ground.

Harry Hopkins

Harry Hopkins is a gardener building a wall it's a small one just about six inches tall commissioned by the lady of the house to remain unnamed in her sixties a genuine gem and widowed since a few years now Harry Hopkins is a bachelor has been a bachelor all his life a rather lanky fellow always liked the ladies likes to make himself useful now and then building a wall six inches small around a tiny lawn how's it coming says the lady of the house standing at the front door cup of tea in hand coming on just fine says Harry Hopkins three more bricks there done today looks like rain just packing up Harry Hopkins looks up to the sky there's no need to work in the rain at his age anyway guess what he's a gardener not a builder and a retired one Harry Hopkins retired no one noticed his many achievements including thirteen ponds twenty-seven patios and an unfinished arboretum this is Harry Hopkins' first wall there's always new challenges in life first replace the front lawn with gravel then build a six inch wall around Harry Hopkins likes a challenge the lady of the house has a nice house she's a nice lady she makes a lovely cup of tea that cat's lovely says Harry Hopkins he always stops to look what I'm doing can't work when that cat's standing there right on the wall Harry Hopkins stands in front of the lady of the house

much taller than her he inclines his head to the side Harry Hopkins planted himself in her garden two years ago has been working on her six inch wall one hour a week for two years so far charging over one thousand pounds Harry Hopkins' eyes drift past her skirt over the front window down to the gravel nothing coming up now says Harry Hopkins nothing to tend nothing to sow you could put some pots there says Harry Hopkins she has no intention to puts some pots there she wants no trouble when Harry Hopkins is finally out of her garden she will close the front door and not open it any more she doesn't want plants she doesn't want grass she doesn't want gardeners in her front garden Harry Hopkins smiles he believes he still has time how many snows will melt and fall how much rain will bounce and squall Harry Hopkins takes the tea pockets the biscuits and the cash I'll eat that later thanks love he says Harry Hopkins inclines his head as if in prayer a bit detached the cat sniffs the gravel the lady of the house sniffs and goes back inside Harry Hopkins puts his head back sniffs the sky looks at his rake sniffs the business end of his rake what is that smell thinks Harry Hopkins sipping his cuppa taking some time off in his break.

Margaret Machiavelli

Margaret Machiavelli no longer gives a fuck with some luck she thinks she will be through it all soon Margaret Machiavelli mainly watches telly sits with her cats on the clawed settee eyes the crochet still to be finished Margaret Machiavelli waits to be finished with this life her Prince has long ago come and gone the kind-eyed stranger who courted and supported Margaret Machiavelli after work on Friday nights and Saturday mornings lying in bed smoking legs akimbo still yawning long ago gone off to the war never more to return Margaret Machiavelli gets a sob in her throat thinking of her Prince in his heavy overcoat a rifle on his shoulder Margaret Machiavelli sees the wars on the telly the children who play in the rubble the cats who hide in the rubble Margaret Machiavelli eyes her will in the open bottom drawer her last will and testament possibly flawed by what Margaret Machiavelli just saw on the telly a pregnant cat and a donkey picking its way through the rubble Margaret Machiavelli suddenly finds sanctuary in the thought that a donkey sanctuary might be a better recourse than leaving her savings to her fickle niece the one with the holiday business and then there's the kids with no parents any more and all the cats and dogs in this country

that need re-homing Margaret Machiavelli last saw her niece 3rd of August 2004 that hot day too hot to do anything else than visit her aunt in her shady quarters each passing year giving Margaret Machiavelli pause to wonder in what respect her niece has earned her legacy especially as time lags so for Margaret Machiavelli time and a Facebook account with one fave from a total stranger on a photo of Geoff her large tom now buried at the bottom of the garden watered with her tears like a rare flower sometimes Margaret Machiavelli feels the power of Geoff while gazing down the garden his hungry mewling his penetrating stare Margaret Machiavelli goes to the drawer and reads over her last will and testament it seems to Margaret Machiavelli that those twenty thousand earmarked for her niece last seen 3rd of August 2004 could be better spent on a sanctuary for cats or on necessary emergency treatment for donkeys Margaret Machiavelli clucks Bonaparte her French cross breed under the chin and chuckles at the thought of the face of her niece on opening the bottom drawer her executrix now receiving one pre-owned settee utterly clawed.

Richard Smart

There's plenty to process with Richard Smart initially you might think he has no heart but on closer acquaintance you discover Richard Smart is all there does not lack any body parts Richard Smart is a fully formed human being whose ears also pop every morning going up to the 52nd floor the view is amazing up there Richard Smart hangs his jacket on the back of the office door and sits down at his computer to read emails about what happened the night before Richard Smart is a believer in people does not put much faith in mathematical laws if we all ran by clockwork says Richard Smart there wouldn't be any sport there wouldn't be any competition Richard Smart has several awards on his wall and a photo of his family in the corner the favourite sport of Richard Smart is golf amongst some others like weights jogging and squash Richard Smart is working on his handicap it is lower now than before but could well be lowered some more Richard Smart gets up and takes a coffee at the machine with his colleagues already he feels part of a team Richard Smart laughs and strokes his silk tie Richard Smart is starting his day with

caffeine it keeps him alert coffee with no milk or expresso as the French would call it americano to Americans Richard Smart is at ease with most names for coffee can generally order whatever coffee he wants also knows how to negotiate deals can put his finger on the strong points and the weak ones Richard Smart opens a dossier and starts to read doesn't know yet what weaknesses and strengths he will find but Richard Smart has faith in himself and believes that only other people make mistakes Richard Smart is thorough and precise there's always room for improvement in his work and life only one year earlier he was on the 43rd floor now he has the 60th in mind Richard Smart tries not to define himself too rigidly does not want to become stuck in some dead-end role admits that his capacity for change is limitless Richard Smart is going up in the world in more senses than one contrary to rumour Richard Smart has a heart he just doesn't show it that would be a mistake Richard Smart doesn't make mistakes and his heart never stops we guess that soon his ears will give a louder pop.

Jo Squires

When Jo Squires first put her pudendum into circulation it was not a very wide one though wider than her immediate circle Jo Squires could not help but feel that such an endeavour deserved more time it was logistically challenging to put your pudendum into circulation like any system of exchange it had to be managed Jo Squires was not beyond the task of managing her own pudendum she immediately saw the benefits of going public and challenged her editors to increase their circulation endeavouring not to count as lost the valuable time she put aside in exchange for their yelps Jo Squires who had always counted herself more fortunate than most now found herself consumed by an interest in statistics a most fortunate development that put her circulation far beyond the bosom of her immediate friends she quickly exchanged her drab circumstances for more contented ones both her pudendum and her bosom figuring large in the overall exchange both rapidly coming to seem valuable assets though Jo Squires found it difficult to put an exact value on them in the short term Jo Squires was certainly talking four figure sums let's call them round numbers and all at once Jo Squires found she had cleared a space in her life for what she loved doing best

Jo Squires was able to visualise herself sitting in the circle of contentment her own statistics had turned into for so many Jo Squires was at the centre of this challenging endeavour to which she now dedicated her entire life though the circle did not seem commensurate with the space she had cleared one day inevitably the word deserving bloomed in her head like a sunflower Jo Squires knew that she would never deserve that space in the same way that space deserved her Jo Squires' capacity for expansion was now well known to be almost infinite she saw no point throwing a veil over it Jo Squires felt like she was living at the centre of a bubble a natural concoction of soap water and air Jo Squires guessed it might all wash off in the rain or it might all come out in the wash Jo Squires was no longer constrained the journey might be a long one those flimsy white spots riding on the backs of black raindrops Jo Squires was sweating now sweating to the very core soaked by spots and glistening black raindrops as if by this superhuman effort of clearing a space for her pudendum she had watered her inner self a watering she now knew she deserved a hole she had dug for herself a kind of well she sobbed into it she could not fill it but it was good to have tried thought Jo Squires though a little rash.

Rylance Robein

Rylance Robein and his partner both worked they had no children at the weekends they had leisure Rylance Robein and his partner found they had plenty of disposable income they were always flying off to pleasure spots in the sun the partner of Rylance Robein said she preferred this kind of life she had no desire to multiply but something was playing in the mind of Rylance Robein ever since Rylance Robein had observed himself in a dream feeding a baby with his own plump breasts it was a most captivating scene also Rylance Robein liked to imagine himself teaching a child to walk putting a baby in a bath full of bubbles Rylance Robein thought he would be able to teach a child to talk after some continual nagging the partner of Rylance Robein agreed to provide a child and nine months later Rylance Robein walked out of a good job working nine to five now Rylance Robein was out of work but felt completely alive in favour with his wife since pulling out his thumb and getting the shopping done Rylance Robein had observed there was no way to find out the flavour of life than to suck it and wanted nothing more than to sit at home with a baby sucking on his chest this was the baby the partner of Rylance Robein had pushed out

of her vagina to donate to Rylance Robein who had no milk in his breasts but could find out how to mix formula and sterilise bottles Rylance Robein saw himself in the role of carer would not get out so much but he would watch television read magazines and pick out ideas for his child Rylance Robein saw himself in the child wanted to make sure the child was turned out nicely the star had risen over the stable of Rylance Robein and the partner of Rylance Robein was in no doubt that Rylance Robein had turned out to be a good carer she could leave in the car for the office assured that Rylance Robein would empty out the dishwasher clean the house do the laundry cook the dinner feed the baby pay the bills Rylance Robein came into all of this cold he found out the hard way with a crying baby in his arms Rylance Robein figured out he could not leave the dream he saw himself in was a pale imitation of reality Rylance Robein looked out from his new reality a young child in his arms remembered going out with his mates after work playing football in the team Rylance Robein went out one afternoon to fetch his child found himself standing in the rain outside the school gate suddenly Rylance Robein glimpsed his own mind it was a dark castle all locked up and he was inside running this way and that looking for routes of escape.

Annie Moe

With Annie Moe it's always donkeys it's always donkeys
or sheep from the moment she wakes to the moment she
sleeps it's always donkeys and dogs or it's hamsters and
budgerigars for Annie Moe in her world of graffiti and
cars her world of bricks and tarmac and wails and alarms
till the weekend is hers and she's off to the city farm with
its acre of grass and creosote barn its fluttering pennants
and wash your hands signs in the stable is where you will
find Annie Moe sweeping the floors and scattering straw
with her donkeys all round they are Derek and Bayleaf
and Gilbert and George looking for treats they nuzzle her
pockets till every carrot's gone a donkey's way and every
donkey the way of a carrot and Annie Moe lives the long
days of love with sheep that baa and cats that purr all her
damp-eyed friends with their well brushed fur till she trots
home at night through the dirty streets back to the flat
where she eats and she sleeps but in Annie Moe's dreams it's
hamsters in the clouds and it's a donkey in the Whitehouse
and budgerigars to advise him and feed him his carrots
and a dog whose nose can drive the donkey's limousine
while all the cats curl up in the back with Annie Moe

beside them their heads laid on her lap but then she wakes and it's Monday and the donkeys her only carrot to be dangled like the prize to get her through the day and all day it's donkey doodling for a bored Annie Moe before it's flying out the concrete yard as evening light begins to fade on city streets she's trotting down to city farm and the creosote barn where there's real donkeys real sheep just grazing relaxing or standing around and she grabs the broom to sweep up straw gathering up its pungent smell on the damp-patched floor and little Annie Moe always the last one to go back to her world of bricks her world of cars with a few blades of straw in her hair she gallops faster than the dogs in their dogged cars all chugged at the lights past the sheep of the pavement heads down grazing cracks and old budgerigars all gazing through security bars in the only world they know of bricks cement and tarmac their world of quick bucks and quick marts of quick bites and sad sights where the face of a donkey hovers over Annie Moe in place of a halo a fond shaggy brow with ears that pivot and a nose that blows warm green grassy air into the life and dreams of Annie Moe.

Mark Berserker

Several years back Mark Berserker discovered KillingStreakUK the online game where he has racked up more than 13,000 deaths an all time record high that will likely not be matched you might say that Mark Berserker has created a mountain of death sometimes in his dreams Mark Berserker sees it as a river of death he sees the bodies floating away face down they look like logs but wearing clothes or sometimes not wearing clothes Mark Berserker has had endless killing sprees at the beach and in the town sometimes the houses look quite real and sometimes the people look quite real as he takes them down they go aaargh or eurghh there is a splatter of blood it is somehow satisfying for Mark Berserker who did not do very well at school yet still considers himself cleverer than most people Mark Berserker had already started playing games at school they said he was a bright lad but introspective one of those boys who sat in the corridor playing games through lunch last year the father of Mark Berserker had a kind of hunch his son could make it big in game play he took him to the UK championships of KillingStreakUK and Mark Berserker cleared the beaches cleared the town and won a cash prize for all the non-combatants he took down Mark Berserker upgraded his graphics card since then

he has been killing more non-combatants even faster his graphics card processing at such blistering speed he had to buy a desktop fan to cool it down however lately Mark Berserker has some doubts he has begun to feel trapped by the transient satisfaction of multiple pointless deaths he feels he would like to have a relationship beyond the circle of his death-addicted friends however it is hard to stop killing sometimes Mark Berserker thinks about deleting his account but the vast tally of death keeps mounting and holds him with an iron grip plus where would he ever find such respect for his achievements again Mark Berserker goes to the refrigerator and takes a cold beer maybe later he will look for a new game Mark Berserker is looking for a new game where death is not part of the formula he is thinking more about beer now he has heard of a game where a small financial risk can lead to large rewards and judging by his previous success he thinks he might be quite good at it Mark Berserker imagines a peaceful life where there is no death a game where he has a mum and dad who love him and a girlfriend who loves him too he will be happy if he can win some financial rewards and buy some beer or even have an online romance a girlfriend in real could be a possibility but after his latest killing spree he doesn't have time to think about that today.

Jeannie Mackay

It's a matter of principle thought Jeannie Mackay as she watched the moon crystallise from behind a cloud it's a matter of principle and a resigning matter thought Jeannie Mackay resigned to the matter her slender hand hesitating over the empty page as thoughts crystallised into words a binding commitment the strong hand of Jeannie Mackay crystallised in commitment shaking a little as if she would shake the hard words onto the empty page a wound that was opening Jeannie Mackay would tend the wound would keep it fresh she was rubbing words into the wound Jeannie Mackay did not let her thoughts drift she would deepen the rift but still her hand hovered there was darkness outside but a light had crystallised inside Jeannie Mackay she was feeling for words in the darkness the right words to express the keenness of her dismay Jeannie Mackay felt the words would be right when she felt them in the darkness they would be rough in a certain way she would know them as she had known them before their certain roughness their certain sharpness only so far only so much only one solution left to Jeannie Mackay a woman who had always loved society the social

34

role but who valued something more her self-respect her dignity Jeannie Mackay knew she was right measured it by her dignity had no other measure than that had no other measure than the hours of service the hours she freely gave did not believe that money was the solution saw that money led to debt saw that debt led to want Jeannie Mackay wanted nothing owed no one Jeannie Mackay loved service and the responsibility of service her strong hand hesitating over the empty page as so many hands had hesitated before Jeannie Mackay could feel those hands on her hand she could name those hands slender and strong pressuring her own plunging her own hand into the wound the bright wound sprinkling salt crystals into the darkness the tender darkness closing over Jeannie Mackay as her slender hand found the certain roughness it was searching for her strong hand closing over the moonlit page forcing the words from her pen's steel nib tearing up the wound the social contract for it's own good the social wound the wound refreshed planting a little pain.

Titus Banville

Here's an excellent fine thing thinks Titus Banville turning it in the palm of his hand a fine old thing clearly a rare old thing thinks Titus Banville lowering himself gently onto a delicate old curule testing it just because it happens to be there just because his fine old legs are happening to become tired Titus Banville lowers his big old behind down onto the delicate curule its legs like interlocking U's that are really the wavy bars of an X an ancient Roman design originally the preserve of emperors consuls praetors censors innocently standing there behind Titus Banville's titanic behind whose legs at that moment of muscular release squeak sharply in terrorised complaint as happens to innocently delicate things and wouldn't thinks Titus Banville it just be an excellent fine thing if he took notice of every squeaking curule every groaning wingback every sighing *fauteuil* that he placed beneath his *Gluteus Maximus* as he calls it sometimes or otherwise when in flamboyant mood his *Chesterfield Tester* his *Pew Splitter* his *Potty Thumper* Titus Banville turns back now to the marvel in hand with a sigh delicately turning the thing in his palm for a better look round descending the interlocking U's of his golden pince-nez to get a better view of the fine detail

the way even the nails are delicately worked in the raised hand all details not lost on Titus Banville whose eyes are still sharp a man who has long since lost his heart to such things as could move by their audacious simplicity or their delicate beauty Titus Banville sits on that Roman-style curule like an emperor might to turn down a thumb at the *Circus Maximus* or a Gulliver might to be measured for new clothes by the diameter of his thumb or a storybook giant might to devour his Tom Thumb or whatever terrorised being he'd just picked up it's just how Titus Banville sees the thing being measured in his palm as if for the first time he sees himself whole and perfectly amazing as he never has before in a tiny human mirror despite angling it this way and that Titus Banville cannot see behind the delicate shield that defends this tiny naked soul Titus Banville cannot help but test the prized ivory's strength just as he has tested the strength of that fine old curule Titus Banville just with a thumbnail prises gently beneath the ivory shield at first no more than a tickle then a gentle forcing and to the surprise of Titus Banville it pops off with a squeak and immediately gets lost somewhere in the folds of his lap as he sees at last what the little he was defending his own callipygian arse.

Leila Abu

That evening her father was finally at peace Leila Abu
knew it when the outside lights flickered she was watching
television her birthright she had always known it would
come to her a small piece of land accompanied by the news
of her father's death in a hospital bed of the sleepless capital
Leila Abu had put some capital aside for this day the day
when all the family would come to bury her father she
remembered how she had visited him at home he said Leila
Abu I've met all the women I want to meet Leila Abu don't
feel sad for me I had all I could handle with a tear in one
eye Leila Abu left down the scratched path of the land he
couldn't handle where he lived all his life among cactuses
Leila Abu wondered about all of the women who'd looked
out of the window at that piece of land her birthright she
wondered if she would one day say I've met all the men I
wanted to meet and had all I could handle would that piece
of land be a birthright for a child of Leila Abu no she would
sell it she would give it away she swore she would cast it
out cactuses and all Leila Abu would continue to follow
her own scratched path out of the arms of the man who
should have been her father who should have acted like a
father lying in a hospital bed like a crack in a dried-out lake

that night her birthright came to her Leila Abu was watching television a film about the latest earthquake how appropriate it was that Leila Abu should watch those houses falling down holes that opened in the ground the devastation of those Richter 7 shakes put everything in perspective and Leila Abu threw open her arms that night she came into the sliver of land and the cactus that stood on the windowsill trying to scratch her hand and Leila Abu winced and couldn't help but toss it out into the night like a chicken bone or a melon skin it sailed into the night and Leila Abu felt chilled her hands began to shake no longer holding her birthright the cactus and the piece of land where her father had kept Leila Abu and all the women he wanted all the time he had wanted them for while the crickets rubbed their legs scritch-scratch the same scritch-scratch Leila Abu had heard all those years before continued still all those women all those nights looking out of the window at the night and one lonely cactus touched by the porch light one lonely cactus beside the winding path he'd thrown into her arms like a snake a sliver of land a patch of useless earth where crickets sawed and scraped.

Werner Hayes

Afraid to be afraid to live as himself in the current moment Werner Hayes reaches backwards in time reaches backwards and takes a glass and a vintage bottle of wine Werner Hayes grasps the elixir of the past still waiting for him on a shelf in a moulded glass bottle in the shape of himself Werner Hayes goes delving in the cellar of time takes one heady draft of the past a fortified wine that tastes of Werner Hayes that smells like Werner Hayes in the halcyon days when his eyes were fresh his hair flicked forward his skin tight as a plucked grape Werner Hayes licks the cool elixir from his lips his eyes close his mouth glistens Werner Hayes listens to the music that the past makes in his own mind his young body bright and honed the various bodies he has owned slender and refined like strong liquor in the mind of Werner Hayes a now fifty-five year old ape with curly brows and hairy ears growing tender in all the wrong places through all the long years Werner Hayes holds up the bottle shaped like Werner Hayes raises it up to his mind watches the past dancing in the liquid glow a river a black river flowing over the land Werner Hayes remembers his youth O vanity O torment O mask worn backwards a kiss on demand for Werner Hayes from who from

himself his young self O youth O callow youth Werner Hayes drifts uneasily on the outer ripples of his mind wheeling back his thoughts to the first big bang Werner Hayes remembers it all crystal clear it gleams in the blackness of intervening years time moving over him like water in the moonlight Werner Hayes moves on moves over moves around is being moved on by time a drifting log a loiterer behind his mask Werner Hayes worn down by the intervening years the youth still glimmering in a crystal glass gleams down the years like moonlight in the water in the black river of time Werner Hayes by the river recalls those sweet times O vanity O torment O deception O youthful deception of sunlight on bronzed limbs of classical façades of kisses in the grass of bodies loved and souls that spilled into each other's glass O heady days of Werner Hayes O bronzed kisses O classical limbs O sunlit façades just one more glass to relinquish all to give up at last to the *aqua vitae* to the *eau de vie* of Werner Hayes a lost soul loitering like moonlight on the river longing for a place of which he does not know the name a swig of life a draft of loss flowing under a bridge he has already crossed.

Sally Meadows

Living by herself on the edge of a small town Sally
Meadows is divorced from her husband divorced from life
Sally Meadows shops cooks does the dishes survives on
the proceeds of redundancy Sally Meadows' reasons to live
include online Scrabble coffee and cheese in all its many
varieties Sally Meadows is not a woman of great notoriety
she is glad to be alone again her husband let her down not
the man Sally Meadows thought him to be the description
initially in her mind did not match the actual contents Sally
Meadows was eventually content to let him go now she has
Scrabble on her mobile and cheese and various unknown
opponents one of whom sends Sally Meadows a photo one
day he is rather suave rather moustachioed Sally Meadows
says so the person says thanks and here's to us and they
play Scrabble and chat and that's how Sally Meadows gets
to hear the problems of a man she doesn't know texting
between Scrabble moves he has bigger problems than
Sally Meadows ever will or so she supposes he tells Sally
Meadows so and Sally Meadows believes him when he
says he is a subsea mechanic he has important work to do
important men to pay important kit to buy but one day he
says he will come and visit Sally Meadows on the edge of
a small town Sally Meadows imagines serving him cheese

stroking his moustachio they will drink coffee their faces turned to the sun and the future Sally Meadows likes this dream and when a small cash flow problem occurs she agrees to pay for an important piece of kit that is needed by the subsurface mechanic Sally Meadows has been bit the biting continues Sally Meadows invests in her dream of a moustachioed smiling man who has now hurt himself in the subsea Sally Meadows pays some health care for this man she does not know who has many more problems than her and responsibilities to finish the work under the sea he will need some money to pay back the money he owes Sally Meadows wants to see her money again she wants to stroke the moustachio and face the sun and the future Sally Meadows is scrabbling now she borrows from her sister she borrows from her mother Sally Meadows makes a last payment to be paid back shortly but the sun goes down on her and the sun rises again and the man disappears Sally Meadows wonders now about the moustachio was it real did anyone go under the sea was any kit bought they are building houses beyond her house Sally Meadows watches the fields disappear wonders how much longer this little house of hers will be hers.

Magnus Herz

What is all the glory of the universe without love thought Magnus Herz all the civilizations all the cultures all the philosophies crumble before the power of love one small flower held in the palm of a child renders them all invisible as air on a summer day in the park Magnus Herz put down his phone started to journey in his mind like a bee on his way back to the hive the sun shone down warming the toes of Magnus Herz he was heading on the journey of his lifetime between the green resplendent trees over the clustered gardens and winding streams Magnus Herz swept along on a twisting breeze the hairs of his body bristling with the thought of this great emotion called love that swelled inside him Magnus Herz slipped through the net of language doubled past the distractions of material things watched them fade like clouds burned up by the sun as Magnus Herz lay in the long hushing grass his mind travelling through the present moment laden down with love happy and forever alive in this moment journeying back to the swarming hive Magnus Herz felt so visible now had crawled slowly out of a dark space the face of his father replaced in his mind by a black hole the shape of his father's fist beating the table telling him to find his life Magnus

Herz had wanted to grasp the fist to clasp his father's mind in his own hands but there had never been a time there had never been a window of opportunity nor a window to fly through and leave it all behind but on this day in this hour Magnus Herz had found the window open wide he felt his tiny wings beat in the breeze Magnus Herz skimmed the greenhouses darted among the dandelion seeds skirted the sweet-smelling bushes in flower Magnus Herz had flirted with joy had bound himself to peace and love at last had found Magnus Herz in this very day this very hour he watched his father's face dim beneath the power of the sun that was guiding him back to the hive Magnus Herz watched his father's fist open like a flower saw the dissolution of his father's dark glower the black hole in his mind flooded with sweet nectar his heart humming praise light as air Magnus Herz journeyed confidently now without a care it was the earth that moved not Magnus Herz the earth rolled under him the hive would come to him with all its sweet power Magnus Herz had only to wait now to voyage far Magnus Herz had given himself up to love.

Robi Rough

Robi Rough thinks she'll go down to the mall it's only a short walk down to the mall where Robi Rough can cash her tokens for a milky coffee splash out on some multi-seeded thins it's just a short walk that will hardly test her shoes the shoes that Robi Rough bought yesterday in the sale but Robi Rough wasn't born yesterday sales are sales she thinks every time I go down to the mall I see a sale I wear out these shoes a little more so now Robi Rough goes barefoot down to the mall the shoes she bought yesterday in her hand and when she nears the portico she sits down slips them on they really are a treat thinks Robi Rough high-heeled slingbacks gold details a little buckle and a band across the heel a small discreet gold flower she strides inside the mall is greeted by a puff of frigid air the doors slide closed behind her and she sees her first new sale in giant letters written SUMMER SALE resist resist she tells herself she sees some gorgeous platforms there but hardly breaks her stride reminds herself about the tokens in her purse the coffee and the multi-seeded thins but gives a token glance into the window rating them as quite desirable say eight out of ten on her personal scale

Robi Rough knows infallibly where everything lies on her personal scale only sometimes Robi Rough does not listen to her own rating it's the case with that girl who works in the mall Robi Rough has the biggest crush on her she is bewitched intoxicated dreads the thought the girl might quit her job one day meanwhile the risk of wearing out her shoes is real the risk of wearing out her heart is all too real for Robi Rough who has already blown enough on platform heels and here's a girl that doesn't even know when Robi Rough clocks onto her she's stacking shirts so nice and crisp so crisp you wouldn't want to ruffle them the girl is nice to Robi Rough she smiles at her so crisp unspoilt you'd want to lay her on the bed thinks Robi Rough and just look down at her you wouldn't want to mess her everything is cool and folded right in place thinks Robi Rough who shortly wanders off and changes out the tokens for some milky coffee thinks I'll have the multi-seeded thins next time the refreshed image of the girl inside her head is sustenance enough and Robi Rough steps outside into brilliant sunshine slips her shoes off walks home with them swinging in her hand.

Biographical notes

Suzanne Smith is a lady who has many interests Suzanne Smith is interested in learning Latin she would like to study Latin at school Suzanne Smith would like to wear a school uniform and carry a hockey stick she thinks that Latin would be fun and hopes that at least some of it would stick Suzanne Smith would like to drop some Latin into her conversations sometimes a well chosen phrase to add a certain *je ne sais pas quoi* Suzanne Smith has glanced through a few relevant textbooks Latin seems a little dry thinks Suzanne Smith somewhat relieved that she has other interests to be going on with such as the history of treating madness Suzanne Smith explains that there is an institution just around the corner from her where they treat madness and interestingly it looks quite similar to the kind of institution where Latin scholars are found.

Jonathan Wonham is a gentleman who has lived locally for some years he is a local author and interested to know if we would be willing to stock his book this being the book that Jonathan Wonham has written and published by himself the name of the book is *Vulgar Variants* and this is the email address of Jonathan Wonham waiting now politely while these words are written down not the words of Jonathan Wonham but the words that are conjured by the embarrassed shop assistant standing opposite Jonathan Wonham who has lived locally since he was eight years old though on a highly discontinuous basis Jonathan Wonham makes no assumptions he will return in one week and smile politely even if the book appears unread and the answer is an apologetic no Jonathan Wonham promises to leave quietly and not break any windows.

Comments on *Ordinary Others*

'Fascinating prose poems and splendid drawings based on a set of invented (or semi-invented?) characters. It is its own peculiar and resonant social world.'

***

'Characters robust and deeply flawed in equal measure. Often abhorrent always desolate and unfulfilled these people are distasteful but extraordinarily intriguing. The beautiful, sad, gnarled illustrations frame each perfectly.'

***

'A remarkable and highly engaging collection: the book is enhanced by black and white illustrations by Suzanne Smith. Quirky and grotesque, they skilfully pick up small details from the poems.'

***

'I read *Ordinary Others* thoroughly from first page to the last, and again, from last page to the first. The omission of punctuation allows that. I enjoyed reading it twice.'

***

'A fabulous read and the illustrations are glorious... a perfect complement.'

***

'A rare set of fanciful tales... Jonathan Wonham has many hats and this peculiar hat fits him very snugly and we wonder what next?'